P.B.Bear's
Favourite
Bedtime Stories

Dorling Kindersley

www.dk.com

Project Editor and Writer Fiona Munro
Art Editor Alexandra Brown
DTP Designer Jill Bunyan
Photography Dave King
Illustration Judith Moffatt
Production Erica Rosen

First published in Great Britain in 2000 by Dorling Kindersley Limited,
9 Henrietta Street, London WC2E 8PS

ISBN 0-7513-5690-5

Colour reproduction by Colourscan
Printed and bound in Italy by L.E.G.O

A CIP catalogue record for this book is
available from the British Library.

The Stories

Goldilocks and the Three Bears

Page 4

Jack and the Beanstalk

Page 10

The Little Red Hen

Page 18

Cinderella

Page 26

The Gingerbread Man

Page 34

The Princess and the Pea

Page 42

GOLDILOCKS AND THE THREE BEARS

On cold winter mornings, my favourite treat is a bowl of delicious hot porridge. Goldilocks likes porridge too. She likes it so much that it gets her into trouble! This is one of my favourite stories because it is all about three bears like me.

ONCE UPON A TIME there were three bears who lived together in a house in the middle of a wood. There was a **great big** bear, a **middle-sized** bear and a teeny-weeny bear.

One day, the three bears made some porridge for breakfast. It was too hot to eat straight away, so they went for a walk in the wood to pass the time until it cooled down.

While the three bears were out, a little girl called Goldilocks came upon the house as she was walking through the wood. She peeped in at the window. Seeing nobody at home, Goldilocks opened the door and stepped inside. She looked about and saw the three bowls of porridge on the table.

There was a **great big** bowl, a **middle-sized** bowl and a teeny-weeny bowl. Goldilocks suddenly felt very hungry. She knew she shouldn't touch the porridge, as it obviously belonged to someone else, but it looked so good she just had to help herself.

First, Goldilocks tasted the porridge in the **great big** bowl. "Ouch!" she cried as it burnt her tongue. "This porridge is very, very hot."

Next, she tasted the porridge in the **middle-sized** bowl. "Yuk!" she said. "This porridge is very, very cold."

Then she tasted the porridge in the teeny-weeny bowl. "Yum!" she said. "This porridge is just right." And she ate it all up.

When Goldilocks had finished, her tummy felt very full. "I think I'll sit down for a few minutes," she said. Goldilocks saw three chairs. There was a **great big** chair, a **medium-sized** chair and a teeny-weeny chair.

First, Goldilocks sat down on the **great big** chair. "This chair is very, very hard," she said, and jumped up.

Next, she sat down in the **middle-sized** chair. "This chair is very, very soft," she said as she struggled to stand up again.

Then Goldilocks sat down on the teeny-weeny chair. "This feels just right," she said. It felt so comfy that she sat on it and sat on it until her bottom went right through!

Next, Goldilocks, who was a bit nosy, went up the stairs and into the bedroom. She saw three beds. There was a **great big** bed, a **middle-sized** bed and a teeny-weeny bed. "I feel sleepy after eating all that porridge," said Goldilocks with a big yawn.

First, she climbed up onto the **great big** bed. It felt uncomfy and a bit lumpy. "I won't fall asleep in this bed," said Goldilocks. "It's too hard." And she climbed down again.

Next, she tried the middle-sized bed. It felt squishy and feathery. "I won't fall asleep in this bed," said Goldilocks. "It's too soft and it makes me sneeze."

"ATCHOOOOO!"

She tumbled out of the bed and onto the floor.

Goldilocks picked herself up and walked over to the teeny-weeny bed and climbed in. "I'll soon fall asleep here," she said. "It feels just right." Goldilocks closed her eyes and snuggled down.

At about the same time as Goldilocks closed her eyes, the three bears came home. They were hungry and looking forward to their breakfast.

"Somebody's been eating my porridge," said the **great big** bear, "and they've left their spoon in it!"

"Somebody's been eating my porridge," said the middle-sized bear, "and they've made a terrible mess!"

"Somebody's been eating my porridge," squeaked the teeny-weeny bear,

"and it's all gone!"

The three hungry bears went to sit down.

"Somebody's been sitting on my chair," said the **great big** bear.
"The cushion's all crooked."
"Somebody's been sitting in my chair," said the **middle-sized** bear.
"The cushion's on the floor."
"Somebody's been sitting on my chair," squeaked the teeny-weeny bear,

"and it's all broken!"

Next, the three bears went upstairs to the bedroom.

"Somebody's been lying in my bed," said the **great big** bear.
"The pillow's all crooked."
"Somebody's been lying in my bed," said the **middle-sized** bear.
"The pillow's on the floor."
"Somebody's been lying in my bed," squeaked the teeny-weeny bear.

"And she's still there!"

The teeny-weeny bear's voice was so squeaky that Goldilocks woke up. She opened her eyes and saw the three bears looking down at her. She was very frightened.

Goldilocks did not stay long enough to find out that the three bears were kind bears. She jumped out of the teeny-weeny bed and ran down the stairs. She ran out of the door as fast as she could and never looked back.

For many mornings to come, the three bears made an extra bowl of porridge just in case Goldilocks came back.

But she never did.

JACK AND THE BEANSTALK

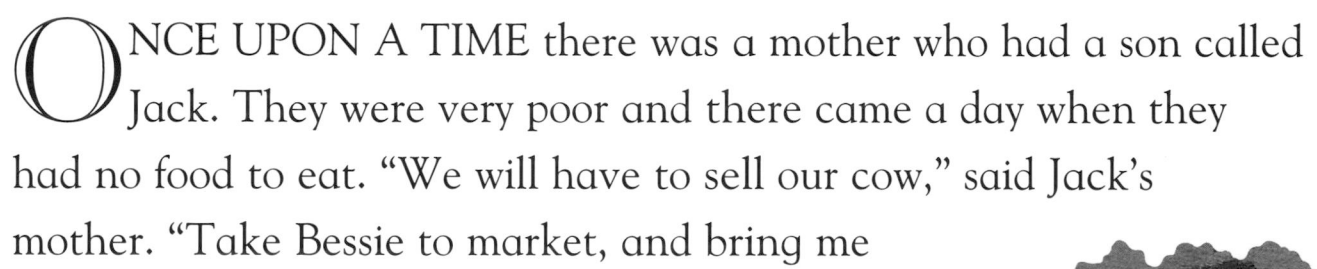

I like to grow things in my garden
but my beans don't grow as fast
or as tall as Jack's do in this story.
I wonder if bears can
climb beanstalks . . .

ONCE UPON A TIME there was a mother who had a son called Jack. They were very poor and there came a day when they had no food to eat. "We will have to sell our cow," said Jack's mother. "Take Bessie to market, and bring me back as much money as you can."

Jack set off. On the way he met a man and stopped for a chat. "That's a fine cow you have there, boy," said the man. "Bessie is a fine, fine cow," said Jack proudly. "But my mother says I am to sell her."

The man looked Bessie over carefully with sharp and sparkly eyes. At last he said, "I'm looking for a cow. Here you are boy. Take these as payment."

He gave Jack a little bag tied with string. Inside, there were five beans. "Excuse me sir," said Jack, who had always been taught to speak politely to strangers, "but how are my mother and I to survive on these?"

"Don't you worry, boy," said the man. "Those are magic beans. You'll never go hungry again."

Jack wasn't sure what the man meant, but he was so pleased to see Bessie go to a good home that he took the beans.

"Thank you," he said, and made his way home.

"You're back quickly," said Jack's mother. "I hope you got a good price for Bessie."

Jack pressed the little bag into his mother's hand. She emptied it onto the table.

"Oh Jack!" she said. "Our cow is gone and all you have to give me in return is five beans. How can I buy food to eat?"

Jack felt very ashamed. His mother opened the kitchen window and threw the beans into the garden. They went to bed hungry that night.

Jack woke early the next morning. When he opened the door, he gasped. Outside was the most enormous beanstalk Jack had ever seen. He looked up and up and up but he couldn't see the top. It disappeared into the clouds.

"The magic beans!" said Jack. "It must have grown from the magic beans!"
Jack began to climb the beanstalk as if it were a ladder.

Higher and higher he went until eventually he reached the top and stepped onto a cloud. In the distance he could see a castle. Jack walked until he reached the big front door. He knocked and a huge woman answered.
"What are you doing here?" she asked. "This is the giant's castle and he eats little boys!"
Jack was very frightened, but he was also very hungry. The woman let him into the warm kitchen.
"Here's some bread and jam. Eat it up and then you must go," she said. Jack ate.
"Where's my breakfast!"
came a booming voice. Jack and the huge woman jumped.
"Quick, hide!" she said. "The giant is coming!"

Jack ran and hid in the log basket. He watched as the giant ate three loaves of bread, two chickens and a **whole** chocolate cake.

"Fetch my gold coins!"

said the giant when he had finished eating. The woman hurried to a huge wooden chest, opened it, took out a small wooden chest and gave it to the giant. Jack watched from his secret place as the giant carefully counted the enormous coins inside. Just a few of those would keep my mother and me fed and clothed for months and months, Jack thought to himself. As he watched, the giant began to doze off. Quick as a flash, Jack climbed up onto the table. With both hands he lifted two of the huge coins, ran out of the room, through the kitchen, out of the door and along the path until at last he saw the top of the beanstalk.

Down
　　and
　　　　down
　　　　　and
　　　　　　　down he climbed with the coins tucked safely under his arm. Jack's mother was very pleased to see him, especially when he showed her the coins, but she made Jack promise that he would never climb the beanstalk again.

After a while Jack and his mother had spent all the money, and Jack couldn't stop thinking about the giant at the top of the beanstalk. One day, when his mother was out, he climbed up to the top again and made his way along the path to the giant's castle. He knocked on the door and the same woman answered.

"The giant is very angry," she said. "Two of his gold coins are missing. If he finds you he will catch you and eat you!"

"Where's my breakfast!" came a booming voice. Jack and the woman jumped. "Quick, hide!" she said. "The giant is coming!" Again, Jack hid in the log basket. He watched as the giant ate three loaves of bread, two chickens and a whole chocolate cake.

"Fetch my golden hen!" said the giant when he had finished eating. The woman hurried to the huge wooden chest and took out a golden hen. The giant said "Lay, golden hen." As Jack watched, the golden hen laid a golden egg. Every time the giant said "lay, golden hen," the hen laid another one.

I must take that hen for my mother, thought Jack. As he watched, the giant began to fall asleep. Quick as a flash, Jack climbed onto the table and scooped up the golden hen. "Cluck cluck cluck," went the hen. The giant stirred in his sleep, but Jack ran out of the room, through the kitchen, out of the door and along the path until at last he saw the top of the beanstalk.

Down
 and
  down
   and
    down he climbed with the golden hen tucked safely under his arm.

Jack's mother was very pleased to see him. The hen laid a golden egg every day, and Jack and his mother were happy. Jack promised her that he would never climb the beanstalk again.

But Jack still couldn't stop thinking about the giant, and one day he climbed, again, to the top of the beanstalk. Again he made his way to the giant's castle and again he knocked on the big door.

"The giant is very angry," said the woman when she answered the door, "because someone has stolen his golden hen. If he finds you he will catch you and eat you!"

"Where's my breakfast!" came the now familiar voice of the giant. Jack and the woman jumped. "Quick, hide!" she said. "The giant is coming!" Again Jack hid in the log basket.

He watched again as the giant ate three loaves of bread, two chickens and a **whole** chocolate cake.

"Fetch my golden harp!" ordered the giant when he had finished eating. The woman hurried to the huge wooden chest and took out a golden harp. Jack heard the most beautiful music. I must take that harp for my mother, he thought to himself.

As Jack watched, the giant began to fall asleep. Quick as a flash, he climbed onto the table and picked up the golden harp. The harp spoke, "Master, master! I am being taken away from you!" The giant opened his eyes.

"Who dares to steal my golden harp?" he roared. Jack was very frightened but he held onto the harp and ran out of the room, through the kitchen and out of the door. He looked around and saw the giant striding along behind him. Jack ran faster and faster along the path until at last he saw the top of the beanstalk.

Down
  and
    down
      and

        down he climbed with the golden harp tucked

safely under his arm. The beanstalk shook as the giant followed Jack down.

"Quick Mother!" shouted Jack. "Fetch the big axe. The giant is coming!"

As soon as Jack reached the ground he took the axe and chopped and hacked and slashed at the beanstalk until, CRASH! It hit the ground. It was so big that it lay over three fields and two hills. The giant crashed to the ground with it and was never seen again.

Jack and his mother used some of their gold to find Bessie and buy her back, and the three of them spent many happy years together listening to the music played by the beautiful golden harp.

THE LITTLE RED HEN

Bedtime is my favourite time of day, but the cat and mouse in this story were always sleeping. The little red hen couldn't get them to help her with anything – until their lives were in danger.

ONCE UPON A TIME in a house on a hill lived three good friends: a cat, a mouse and a little red hen. Inside their house, it was warm and cosy. The cat slept on a chair by the fire, the mouse slept in a hole in the skirting board and the little red hen slept wherever she found herself. When she wasn't sleeping, the little red hen was cleaning and cooking and dusting and polishing the little house. The cat and the mouse were always sleeping.

One bright morning, the little red hen woke up, hopped down from a chair and fluffed up her feathers. "Who will go shopping for our breakfast?" she asked her friends, cat and mouse. "I'm far too busy," said the cat as she gave a big yawn, curled

up in a tight ball and went back to sleep.
"I haven't got time," said the mouse
from her bed of straw.
"Then I shall just have to go myself,"
said the little red hen.

"Who will go to the well and collect
water for the washing?" asked the little
red hen.
"I'm far too busy," said the cat from her cosy cushion by the fire.
"I haven't got time," said the mouse as she stretched her warm furry
body and settled down to sleep.
"Then I shall just have to go myself," said the little red hen.

Off she set with a basket for the shopping and a pail for the water.

On the other side of the hill stood a very old and scruffy house. The
paint was peeling off the walls and tall weeds grew in the little
garden. A mean old mother fox and her sly young son lived there.

"Mother, I'm hungry," said the sly young fox.

"The cupboard is bare," said the mean old mother fox, "but I have an idea. The little red hen, from the house on the other side of the hill, has just gone out with a pail and a basket. That means the lazy cat and the lazy mouse will be all alone. I feel like stewed cat and stewed mouse for supper."

The sly young fox smiled and his furry tummy rumbled.

"Take this sack," said the mean old mother fox, "and capture them before the little red hen comes home. I'll build a fire and put on a big pot of water to boil, ready to cook the cat and the mouse."

The sly young fox took the sack and set off towards the house on the other side of the hill.

Tap, tap, tap.

"Who's that knocking on our door?" asked the lazy cat.

"The little red hen will see who it is," replied the lazy mouse.

"She's out shopping and getting water," said the cat.

"You see who it is. You're nearer," said the mouse.

The cat jumped off her chair, walked to the door, and turned the big handle.

"Hello," said the sly young fox to the cat. "What a lovely home you and your friends have. May I come in?" He pushed past the cat and walked into the warm kitchen. Then he opened his big sack, scooped up the cat, and threw her into it. Then he scooped up the mouse and threw her in too.

The cat and the mouse were very frightened. It was dark.

They held each other's paw, which made them feel safer.

Just as the sly young fox was leaving the house with his bulky sack, the little red hen came running home.

"SQUAWK, SQUAWK!"

"What are you doing here, Mister Fox?" she cried. "And where are my good friends, cat and mouse?"

"In this sack!" said the sly young fox with a smile. "I'm taking them home for my mother and me to eat for our supper . . .

AND NOW I'M GOING TO TAKE YOU TOO!"

The little red hen flapped and squawked and squawked and flapped, as the sly young fox picked her up in his big furry paws and dropped

her into the sack. It was very heavy now but he picked it up, threw it over his shoulder and walked off towards the other side of the hill.

"I'm so frightened," squeaked the mouse. "I don't want to be anyone's supper!"

"My feathers are getting ruffled in this horrible sack," squawked the little red hen.

"What are we to do?" said the cat to her friends. "How can a cat, a mouse and a little red hen escape from a sly young fox?"

Suddenly, the friends heard the fox say, "It's such a sunny day, and this sack is so heavy. I think I'll just sit under this tree and rest for a while."

He put his sack on the ground and sat down. Before long he dozed off. zz...zz...zz...zz...zz...ZZ...ZZ...ZZ...ZZ.

Inside the sack, the little red hen was thinking hard. "Who will help me escape?" she whispered.

"I will!" said the cat.

"I will!" said the mouse.

"Who has sharp teeth,"

asked the little red hen, "to gnaw a hole in the sack?"

"I have sharp teeth!" said the mouse. "I'll gnaw a hole in the sack."

"And who has a bright pair of eyes," asked the little red hen, "to watch the sly young fox in case he wakes up?"

"I have a bright pair of eyes," said the cat. "I'll watch the sly young fox."

So the mouse gnawed and gnawed and the cat watched and watched. Soon there was a big enough hole in the sack for all the friends to clamber through.

Together, they found a big stone and rolled it and pushed it and pushed it and rolled it into the sack. The little red hen took a needle and thread from under her wing and neatly stitched up the hole. Then, the three friends ran back to their little house and locked the door.

A while later, the sly young fox woke up and gave a big yawn. He picked up the sack and made his way home. His mean old mother was waiting for him. "You've been gone such a long time!" she said. "And I'm very hungry. Did you find the cat and the mouse?"

"I did," said the sly young fox proudly. "And the little red hen!"

"YUM YUM!" she said, licking her lips.

The mean old mother fox picked up the heavy sack and turned it upside down above the pot of boiling water.

SPLASH! went the big stone.

"Where are the mouse and the cat and the little red hen?" she cried.

"They've escaped!" said the young fox. "How could a cat and a mouse and a little red hen have escaped from a sly fox like me?"

The mean old mother fox was very angry with her foolish young son, and they both went to bed that night with rumbling tummies.

Cinderella

I love parties, don't you? Imagine how sad Cinderella felt when she wasn't invited to the ball. She spent every day working hard for her bossy stepsisters and never had any fun, but everything changed when she discovered that she had a fairy godmother.

O NCE THERE WAS A GIRL who lived happily with her mother and father until one sad day her mother became ill and died. She missed her very much and was happy when a few years later her

father married again. The girl's stepmother had two daughters of her own, but they were unfriendly and very, very bossy. It was left to the girl to do all the housework and the cooking on her own. Her stepsisters called her Cinderella because her clothes were always covered with soot and cinders from the fire, but Cinderella never complained.

One morning a royal messenger knocked on the door and handed

Cinderella two envelopes. "Invitations to the Prince's Grand Ball from the King and Queen," he said. Cinderella was very disappointed when she read the names on the envelopes. There was no invitation for her. Everyone thought of her as just a servant, dressed in rags, not as a young lady fit to dance with a prince.

Cinderella's stepsisters became more and more excited as the day of the ball drew near. There were gowns to make, jewels to try on and shoes to buy. Poor Cinderella was exhausted. She spent half the night stitching instead of sleeping.

At last the day of the ball arrived and the sisters began to get ready. Cinderella brushed their hair, polished their jewels, pulled and pushed them into their new gowns and squeezed and shoved them into their new shoes. By the time they had swept out of the house there was so much mess to clear up Cinderella was almost in tears. She sat down by the fire and wept. Suddenly she heard a voice . . .

"What's that terrible noise?" it said.

Cinderella looked up and there in front of her stood the

kindest-looking lady she had ever seen. She was smiling, and Cinderella thought how much she looked like the mother she had almost forgotten.

"Why are you crying? I'm your fairy godmother and I might be able to help." Cinderella blew her nose. "My two stepsisters have gone to the ball at the Palace. I wasn't invited, because everybody thinks I am just a servant girl and not good enough to dance with a prince."

Cinderella's fairy godmother smiled. "You shall go to the ball," she said. Cinderella looked down at her ragged clothes and her dirty shoes. "But I haven't a **thing** to wear!" she said.

Her fairy godmother waved a magic wand. Before her eyes, Cinderella's ragged dress turned into a gown made from jewel-coloured silks and real silver sequins, while her old shoes became slippers of the most delicate glass.

"That's better!" she said. "Now. We need to get you to the ball. What's in the larder?"

"Only a pumpkin to make into soup," said Cinderella.

"That's perfect," said her fairy godmother. She waved her magic wand again and the pumpkin turned into a magnificent coach. Cinderella could hardly believe what was happening.

With another wave of the wand, six scuttling mice were turned into six prancing white horses.

"Now we just need coachmen and a driver," she continued. In an instant two spiders and a lizard were turned into uniformed attendants.

"Now you're ready to go!" said Cinderella's fairy godmother at last.

"Oh thank you," said Cinderella.

"Now listen very carefully to what I am about to tell you," said her fairy godmother. "Watch the big clock at the Palace and make sure you leave the ball before it strikes midnight. When the clock strikes twelve, your coach will turn back into a pumpkin."

"I promise," said Cinderella. She kissed her fairy godmother, picked up her skirts and, in her glass slippers, stepped into the pumpkin coach. The horses galloped towards the Palace.

When Cinderella arrived at the Ball she saw ladies wearing beautiful gowns and glittering jewels, and she saw lots of handsome men. One of them seemed to her more handsome than all the others. He saw her, walked across the room, and led her onto the dance floor. Cinderella felt so happy that her feet in their glass slippers barely touched the ground. She looked around and noticed that several of the other guests were staring at her.

Cinderella danced with the handsome young man all evening, and she forgot all about the time. Suddenly, when the palace clock began to chime she remembered her promise, but it was too late. The clock chimed 8 . . . 9 . . . 10 . . . 11 . . . 12.

Cinderella ran from the ballroom and down the palace steps, losing one of her beautiful glass slippers on the way.

She saw several elegant coaches waiting, but she couldn't see *her* golden coach anywhere – just a pumpkin lying in the gutter and six mice, two spiders and a lizard scurrying into the dark. Cinderella began to cry when she glanced down and saw that her beautiful gown had disappeared. Instead she stood in her old tattered dress. She picked up the pumpkin and ran home as fast as she could.

The next morning the whole town was talking about the ball. A lot of the talk was about Cinderella.

"Did you see that girl in the dress with the silver sequins?" one of Cinderella's stepsisters was asking the other. "I'm sure they weren't **real** silver. I hated it and I'm sure the Prince did too." "But he danced with her all evening," scoffed the other.
"Luckily she disappeared," they explained to Cinderella. "But after that the Prince didn't seem to be enjoying himself. I think it was because he couldn't make up his mind between you and I sister!"

Cinderella suddenly realised that the man she had been dancing with was the Prince and that if she ever met him again he wouldn't recognise her in her tattered dress with soot on her face. She was heartbroken, and a great big tear rolled down her face.

"What is the matter, you silly girl?" spat the sisters.

A few hours later there was a knock on the door. Cinderella opened it. There stood the Prince. "Hello," he said. "I have here a glass slipper. One of the guests at the ball left it behind and I would like to return it." Cinderella looked into his eyes and realised that she had been right. He had no idea they had met before. Her stepsisters barged past her. "Oh, your royal highness!" they began. "How wonderful of you to drop by. We so enjoyed the ball last night. What is that you have there? Is it a gift?"

"It's a glass slipper," he said. "Someone left it behind last night. I would very much like to marry the girl who was wearing it. Never before have I met anyone so enchanting and beautiful. Ladies, would you do me the honour of trying the slipper?"

The sisters didn't have to be asked twice. They fought to be the first to try to cram their foot into the delicate slipper.

"It's bound to fit me," said one.

"It's far too small for you. It was made for a delicate foot such as mine," said the other. The slipper didn't fit either of the sisters. "What about you?" said the Prince, looking at Cinderella. "Will you try the slipper?"

"HER!" laughed the stepsisters. "You want Cinderella to try the slipper! Cinderella is our maid. She wasn't even at the ball! She was here by the fire doing the mending. Ha ha ha!"

But Cinderella had recognised the glass slipper and, stepping forward, slipped her tiny foot into it. A perfect fit.

The screams and cries of Cinderella's stepsisters could, they say, be heard in the next country. The Prince took his future bride's hand and together they walked through the town and up the steps of the Palace, with the cheers of the people all around them.

That evening, Cinderella's stepsisters ate their pumpkin soup by themselves.

THE GINGERBREAD MAN

I like baking biscuits and sharing them with my friends. In this story everybody wants a share of the gingerbread man, but they've got to catch him first!

THERE ONCE WAS AN OLD LADY who lived by herself. One day, she was sitting thinking about how lonely she was when she had an idea. She went into her kitchen and found some flour, some sugar, some butter and some ginger.

"I will **make** myself a friend!" she said. The old lady mixed all the ingredients together in a bowl and then rolled the mixture out. She found a knife and carefully cut out the shape of a little man. She gave him chocolate drops for eyes and a mouth, and raisins for buttons.

"You will make a fine friend for me," she said.

The old lady popped the gingerbread man into the oven and waited.

Before long, she smelt a delicious smell. "My gingerbread man is ready!" she said, and opened the oven door. But before she could lift him out of the oven, the gingerbread man had jumped down onto the floor and run out of the door. As she watched, he ran across the garden, out of the gate and down the lane. The old woman picked up her skirts and followed him as quickly as she could. "Come back, gingerbread man," she cried. As he disappeared out of sight, she heard him call out.

"Run, run, as fast as you can!

You can't catch me, I'm the gingerbread man!"

The gingerbread man ran down the lane and into the field where there was a cow.

"That gingerbread man looks very tasty," said the cow. "I think I'll eat him up. Come here, gingerbread man!" he mooed. "I'm hungry!" But the gingerbread man kept on running and called back to the cow,

"Run, run, as fast as you can!

You can't catch me, I'm the gingerbread man!"

The gingerbread man ran faster and faster. The old lady ran after him and the cow ran after the old lady. Soon, the gingerbread man came to a gate. He ran underneath it, the old lady opened it, and

the cow ambled through it. On the other side was another field where a horse was grazing. The horse heard the commotion and saw the gingerbread man.

"That gingerbread man looks very tasty," said the horse. "I think I'll eat him up. Come here, gingerbread man!" he neighed. "I'm hungry!"

But the gingerbread man kept on running and called back to the horse,

"Run, run, as fast as you can!

You can't catch me, I'm the gingerbread man!"

The gingerbread man ran faster still. The old lady followed him, the cow trotted behind her, and the horse galloped behind the cow. Soon, the gingerbread man came to a high hedge. He found a little hole and clambered through. The old lady found a big hole and followed him. The cow followed her through the hole and the horse jumped clean over it.

The gingerbread man stopped. Straight in front of him was a wide river. "I can't swim!" he cried. "What will I do? The old lady, the cow and the horse will catch me and eat me!"

Out of the thick undergrowth there came a sly, slinky fox.
"I can swim very well," he said to the gingerbread man.
"Let me help you across the wide river."

"Oh, thank you!" said the gingerbread man and he jumped onto
the fox's bushy tail.

The fox began to swim across the wide river. His tail swished from
side to side through the water. "You can't be very comfortable," he

said to the gingerbread
man, who was holding on
as tightly as he could.
"Why don't you stand on
my back instead?"
The gingerbread man slowly
crawled up the fox's bushy tail
and onto his smooth back. They
were approaching the middle of
the river. "It's getting deeper,"
said the fox. "Why don't you
stand on my head so that
you don't get wet?"

The gingerbread man
crept up the fox's neck
until he was sitting on top
of his head.

"It's very windy and I'd hate you to fall into the river," said the fox. "Why don't you come and sit on the end of my nose?"

The gingerbread man carefully slithered down the fox's long nose until he was balancing right on the very very end of it.

"You smell delicious!" said the fox.

"I'm going to eat you all up!"

The clever fox moved even faster than the gingerbread man. He tossed his head back, throwing the poor gingerbread man high up into the air. Then he opened wide his great big mouth, showing his great big teeth, and the poor gingerbread man landed right in between them.

"Yum, yum!"

said the fox as he crunched up the

gingerbread man and licked his lips. Soon, the gingerbread man was all gone.

He had been too clever for the old woman, too clever for the cow, and too clever for the horse.

But he was not nearly clever enough for the sly, slinky fox.

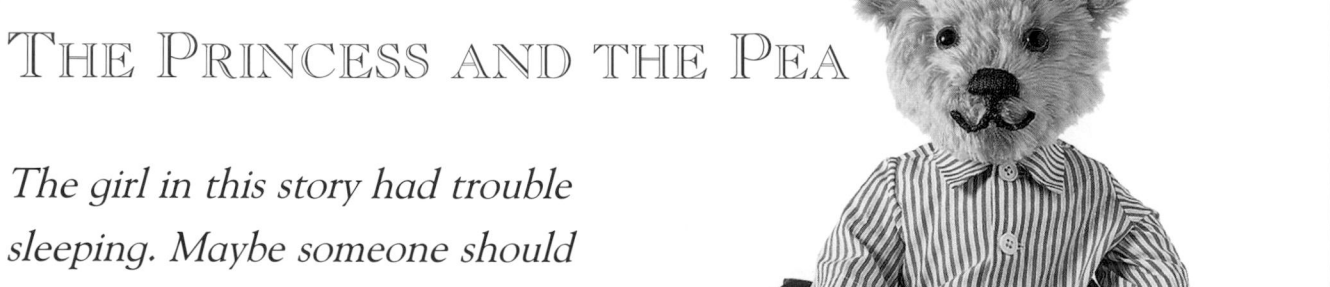

THE PRINCESS AND THE PEA

The girl in this story had trouble sleeping. Maybe someone should have read her a bedtime story like this one. Good night and sleep tight!

ONCE UPON A TIME there was a King and a Queen and a Prince. They lived in a beautiful castle in a perfect land where the sun was always shining and people were always smiling. Well, everyone smiled apart from the Prince. He was getting to the age where he thought he should be married, but he just couldn't find the perfect princess. There were lots of princesses to choose from, but not one of them was quite right. The King and Queen were beginning to wonder what was to become of their handsome son. They hosted glittering parties, inviting princesses from all over the world, and the Prince danced with them

all and charmed them all until every one of them had fallen a little bit in love with him.

The morning after every party, the King and Queen would sit at the breakfast table with the Prince and wait for him to tell them that he had found the perfect princess and fallen in love with her. But he never did. He would say how beautiful one was, and how amusing another was, but he never said that she was the one, the perfect princess. The royal family despaired. They had entertained almost all the princesses in the world.

One night when everybody in the palace was asleep a huge storm blew up.

The wind howled around the battlements and rain lashed against the windows. The Queen was just thinking about going to make some cocoa when she heard a faint tapping on the great castle door. She listened for a few minutes in case she was mistaken, and then heard the noise again. She climbed out of bed, tiptoed down the sweeping staircase and opened the door.

There stood a soaking wet and bedraggled girl. She explained to the Queen that she was a princess and that she was lost. The Queen invited the girl inside and set about finding her some dry clothes.

When the girl had dried off, changed her clothes and was eating some supper, the

Queen herself went to prepare a room for her. She placed a tiny green dried pea on the base of the bed and then opened a cupboard and one by one took out twenty feather mattresses which she put on the bed, on top of the pea.

Soon the girl was ready for bed. She looked a little bit surprised when she saw where she was to sleep, but was so tired that she quickly climbed up on top of the highest mattress and closed her eyes. The Queen blew out the candle and bid the girl pleasant dreams.

In the morning, the girl found her way down the sweeping staircase and into the dining room. The Queen had told the King and the Prince about the strange girl who claimed to be a princess

and they were very curious to see her. As soon as the girl entered the room the Prince stood up. Could she be **the one**, the perfect princess? he thought to himself.

"How did you sleep, my dear?" asked the Queen as the girl sat down at the table.

Now the girl was not sure how to answer this question as she did not want to be ungrateful, but she had always been taught to tell the truth.

"I didn't sleep well at all," she said at last. "The feather mattresses were soft and the quilts were warm and cosy, but there was a lump in the bed that was very uncomfortable."

The Queen smiled. "You are indeed a princess," she said, "and a very special one at that."

"Am I?" replied the girl.

"Is she?" said the Prince who was already beginning to fall in love with this beautiful girl.

"Oh yes!" said the Queen. "Last night I placed a small dried pea beneath twenty feather mattresses, and no one but an unusually sensitive and perfect princess would be able to feel it."

The Princess tried not to laugh, but she had to smile. And when the Prince saw her beautiful smile he knew he had at last found his bride.

Good night

P.B. Bear